VOCAL SCORE

RUDDIGORE

OR
THE WITCH'S CURSE

BY

W. S. GILBERT

AND

ARTHUR SULLIVAN

© Chappell Music Ltd.,
© International Music Publications Limited
Griffin House, 161 Hammersmith Road, London W6 8BS, England

RUDDIGORE

OR

THE WITCH'S CURSE

DRAMATIS PERSONÆ.

MORTALS.

SIR RUTHVEN MURGATROYD (*Disguised as Robin Oakapple, a Young Farmer*)

RICHARD DAUNTLESS (*His Foster-Brother—A Man-o'-wars-man*)

SIR DESPARD MURGATROYD (*Of Ruddigore—A Wicked Baronet*)

OLD ADAM GOODHEART (*Robin's Faithful Servant*)

ROSE MAYBUD (*A Village Maiden*)

MAD MARGARET

DAME HANNAH (*Rose's Aunt*)

ZORAH } (*Professional Bridesmaids*)
RUTH

GHOSTS

SIR RUPERT MURGATROYD (*The First Baronet*)

SIR JASPER MURGATROYD (*The Third Baronet*)

SIR LIONEL MURGATROYD (*The Sixth Baronet*)

SIR CONRAD MURGATROYD (*The Twelfth Baronet*)

SIR DESMOND MURGATROYD (*The Sixteenth Baronet*)

SIR GILBERT MURGATROYD (*The Eighteenth Baronet*)

SIR MERVYN MURGATROYD (*The Twentieth Baronet*)

AND

SIR RODERIC MURGATROYD (*The Twenty-first Baronet*)

CHORUS OF OFFICERS, ANCESTORS, VILLAGERS, AND PROFESSIONAL BRIDESMAIDS

Act I.—The Fishing Village of Rederring, in Cornwall.

Act II.—Picture Gallery in Ruddigore Castle.

RUDDIGORE

OR

THE WITCH'S CURSE

CONTENTS.

RUDDIGORE

OR
THE WITCH'S CURSE

Words by
W. S. GILBERT

Music by
ARTHUR SULLIVAN

OVERTURE
(Arranged by GEOFFREY TOYE)

Chappell

Tempo I

Allegretto grazioso

Chappell

Chappell

Chappell

6

f marcato

Act 1

Nº 1 CHORUS OF BRIDESMAIDS — (Solo Soprano, Zorah)

Chappell

CHORUS OF WOMEN
SOPRANOS

CHO.

CHO.

Chappell

CHO. mar - ry you to - day?

mar - ry you to - day?

SOLO. ZORAH

Ev - 'ry — day, as the days roll on, Brides-maids' garb we gai - ly don,

ZORAH

Sure that a maid so — fair - ly famed Can't long re - main un - claimed.

ZORAH

Hour by — hour, and day by day, Sev - 'ral — months have passed a - way,

Chappell

12

ZORAH: Though she's the fair-est flow'r that blows, No one has mar-ried Rose!

CHO.: Rose, all glow - ing With vir-gin blush-es, say — Is

CHO.: an-y-bo-dy go - ing To mar-ry you to - day?

18311

Chappell

Chappell

14

Chappell

SONG—(Hannah) and CHORUS

16

18311   Chappell

Chappell

Chappell

No. 3   SONG–(Rose)

20

18311   Chappell

22

N.° 4 DUET—(Rose and Robin)

18311   Chappell

Chappell

24

Chappell

Chappell

Nᵒˢ 5 & 6 CHORUS OF BRIDESMAIDS AND SONG—(Richard)

Chappell

Chappell

28

18311   Chappell

Chappell

№ 6a

HORNPIPE

SONG — (Robin, with Richard)

№ 7

Chappell

 Chappell

Chappell

N̲o̲ 8

DUET – (Rose and Richard)

Chappell

№ 9　　　　ENTRANCE OF BRIDESMAIDS

Chappell

BRIDESMAIDS

No 10   TRIO—(Rose, Richard, and Robin)

Chappell

Chappell

40

18311

Chappell

Chappell

RECIT. and ARIA–(Margaret)

46

18311

MARG.

the wan-ton ro - ses, Who, up-ris-ing from their beds, Hold on high their shame-less
up-on her pe - tals, Though she lived a-lone, a - part, Hope lay nest-ling at her

MARG.

heads With their pret-ty lips a-pout-ing, With their pret-ty lips a-pout-ing, Nev-er
heart, But, a - las, the cruel a-wak-ing, But, a - las, the cruel a-wak-ing Set her

MARG.

doubt-ing, nev - er doubt-ing That for Cy-the-re-an po -
lit - tle heart_____ a - break-ing, For he ga-ther'd for his po -

MARG.

-sies He would ga-ther aught but ro - ses! 2. In a
-sies On - ly ro - ses, on - ly ro - - - ses!

Chappell

48

N⁰ 12

CHORUS

Chappell

Chappell

50

sud-den tran-si-tion Is sim-ply E-ly-sian, Come, A-ma-ryl-lis, Come, Chlo-e and Phyl-lis, Your

slaves, for the mo-ment, are we! _____ Your slaves, _____ for _____ the

mo- ment, ___ your slaves _____ are we!

GIRLS

The sons of the tillage Who dwell in this village Are peo-ple of low-ly degree—degree, Though

hon-est and act-ive They're most un-at-tract-ive And awk-ward as awk-ward can be— can be. They're

Chappell

GIRLS: clum-sy clod-hop-pers With ax-es and choppers, And shep-herds and ploughmen And drovers and cow-men,

GIRLS: Hedg-ers and reapers, And carters and keepers, But nev-er a lov-er for me,___ But nev - er a

GIRLS: lov - er___ for me! Heart-y greet - ing of-fer

MEN: Then come, A-ma-ryl-lis, Come, Chloe and Phyllis,

GIRLS: we, of - fer we!___ So wel - come, gen - try,

MEN: When thor-ough-ly tir-ed Of be-ing ad-mir-ed By

f

mf

p marcato

Chappell

52

18311

Chappell

Chappell

18311

Chappell

Chappell

56

18311

Chappell

Chappell

Chappell

Nº 14 DUET—(Richard and Sir Despard)

Allegro vivace

Piano

RICHARD, 1st Verse

You un - der-stand?

RICHARD, 2nd Verse

Like-wise the Bride—The maid-ens are ve - ry E - lat - ed and mer-ry; They

Sir DESPARD, 1st Verse

I think I do, With vi - gour un-shak-en This step shall be ta - ken, It's

Sir DESPARD, 2nd Verse

The Bride-groom comes—

Chappell

60

Chappell

Chappell

№ 15

FINALE — ACT I

Chappell

GIRLS
Smil-ing sum-mer beams up-on— her
Ped.
GIRLS
Shed-ding ev-'ry bles-sing on— her: Maid-ens, greet her - Kind-ly treat her - You may all— be
B
GIRLS
brides some day!
MEN f
Hail the Bride-groom who— ad - van - ces, A - gi - ta - ted, Yet e -
mf
MEN
- la - ted. He's in eas - y cir - cum - stan - ces, Young and lust - y, True— and

64

Chappell

66

18311

Chappell

Chappell

68

Chappell

Chappell

70

18311

Chappell

Chappell

72

CHO.

la la la la la la! Fa la la la la la la la la la!

la la la! Fa la la la la la la!

la la la! Fa la la la la la la!

la la la la la! Fa la la la la la la!

L'istesso tempo

18311

Chappell

Chappell

Chappell

Chappell

76

18311

Chappell

Chappell

78

18311   Chappell

Chappell

Chappell

Chappell

Andante

Chappell

Chappell

Chappell

Chappell

ROBIN: And wretched the let-ter That no one can read! But ve - ry much bet-ter Their

ROBIN: lot it must be Than that of the per-son I'm mak - ing this verse on, Whose

ROBIN: head there's a curse on—Al - lu - ding to me!

CHORUS
Oh, happy the li - ly When kiss'd by the bee; And, sipping tran-quil-ly, Quite hap - py is he;
Oh, happy the li - ly When kiss'd by the bee; And, sipping tran-quil-ly, Quite hap - py is he;
Oh, happy the li - ly When kiss'd by the bee; And, sipping tran-quil-ly, Quite hap - py is he;
Oh, happy the li - ly When kiss'd by the bee; And, sipping tran-quil-ly, Quite hap - py is he;

Chappell

90

CHO.

And happy the filly That neighs in her pride; But happier than a-ny A pound to_ a pen-ny, A

And happy the filly That neighs in her pride; But happier than a-ny A pound to a pen-ny, A

And happy the filly That neighs in her pride; But happier than a - ny A pound to a pen - ny, A

And happy the filly That neighs in her pride; But happier than a-ny A pound to a pen-ny, A

CHO.

lo - ver is, when he Em-bra - ces his bride!___ Em-bra - ces his

lo - ver is, when he Em-bra - ces his bride!___ Em-bra - ces his

lover is, when he Em-bra - ces his bride!___ Em-bra - ces his

lo - ver is, when he Em-bra - ces his bride! Em-bra - ces his

Chappell

92

18311

Chappell

END OF ACT I
Chappell

Act II.

DUET–(Sir Ruthven and Adam)

Andante moderato

Piano

Chappell

18311

Chappell

№ 2   DUET — (Rose and Richard) and CHORUS OF GIRLS

98

RICH. you are the fair-est, The rich-est and rar-est Of in-no-cent lass-es you are, By far—

RICH. — Of in-no-cent lass-es you are! Fanned by a fa-vour-ing

RICH. gale, You'll sail O-ver life's treach-er-ous sea With me, And as for bad wea-ther We'll

RICH. brave it to-geth-er, And you shall creep un-der my lee, My wee!

RICH. And you shall creep un-der my lee,— My wee!———— For you

 Chappell

100

18311

Chappell

ROSE & RICHARD

ROSE &
RICH.

Chappell

No 3   SONG—(Rose, with Chorus of Girls, Sir Ruthven and Richard.)

Chappell

106

Chappell

CHO.

cus - tomed place ___ Steps in - to the world once ___ more!

TENORS

CHO.

Baronet of Ruddigore, Last of our ac - cur - sed line,
BASSES

Down up-on the oaken floor —

108

CHO.

Down up-on those knees of thine! Cow-ard, pol-troon, sha-ker, squeamer,

CHO.

Blockhead, sluggard, dul-lard, dreamer, Shirk-er, shuf-fler, crawl-er, creep-er,

CHO.

Snif-fler, snuf-fler, wail-er, weep-er, Earthworm, mag-got, tad-pole, wee-vil!

Chappell

Sir RUT. thus, with i-cy glare __ And stern re-lent-less brow, __ Ap-pear-est, who knows how?

Sir RODERIC I am the spectre of the late Sir Roderic Mur-ga-troyd, Who

Sir ROD. comes to warn thee that thy fate Thou canst not now a-void.

Sir RUTHVEN A-las, poor ghost!

Sir RODERIC The pi-ty you Express, for nothing goes: We spec-tres are a jol-lier crew Than

Sir ROD you, per-haps, sup-pose! We spec-tres are a jol-lier crew Than you, per-haps, sup-pose!

CHORUS

Attacca

Chappell

SONG–(Sir Roderic) and CHORUS

Chappell

Chappell

116

18311   Chappell

Chappell

No 6

CHORUS

Chappell

 Chappell

Chappell

№ 7   DUET—(Margaret and Despard)

DES.

But be   so kind To bear   in mind,   We were the vic-tims of

MARG.

cir - cum-stan-ces!

MARG.

That   is one of our blame-less dan-ces.

2nd verse

I was

MARG.

once an ex - ceed-ing-ly odd young la - dy —   Suf-fer-ing much from spleen and va-pours.

124

18311   Chappell

Chappell

N<u>o</u> 8   TRIO–(Margaret, Sir Ruthven, and Despard)

128

18311

Chappell

Chappell

130

18311   Chappell

132

18311   Chappell

Chappell

134

Nº 9

MELODRAME

Piano

Allegro

(During dialogue)
Agitato

CODA

18311

Chappell

N.º 10   SONG.-Hannah (with Sir Roderic)

    Chappell

Chappell

FINALE – ACT II

138

18311

Chappell

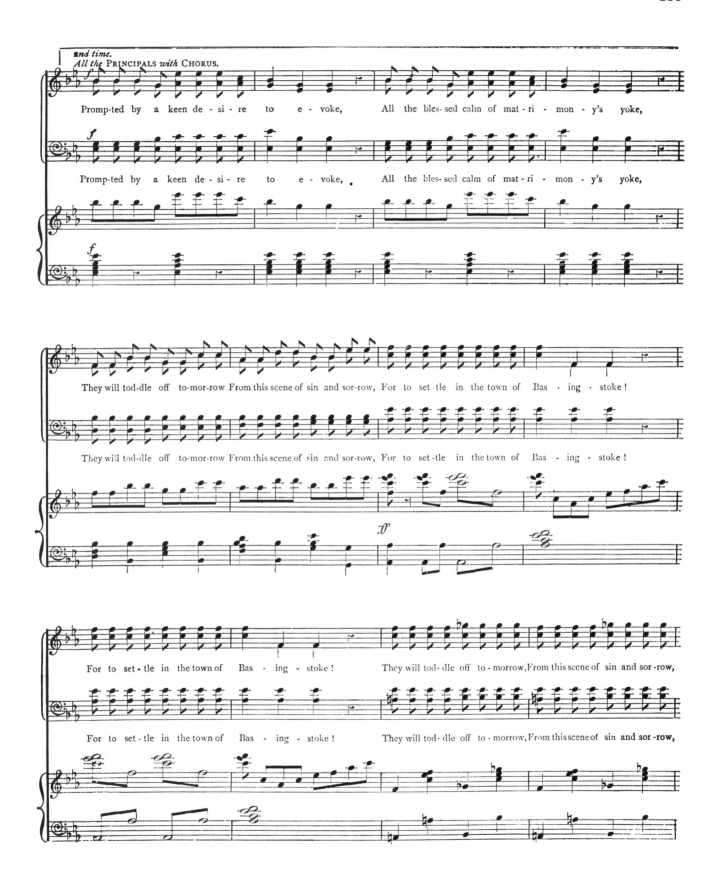

140

18311

Chappell

End of Opera.

Chappell